The Collectors' Book of

DAVID WINTER COTTAGES™

Published by
John Hine Ltd.

Designed by
John Hine Creative Ltd.

Art Director:
Tony Hanlon

Editor:
John Tiley

With thanks to
Period Home
Magazine Ltd.

Printed by
Morcombe Printers,
Romsey,
Hampshire.

David Winter Cottages

John Hine describes his personal feeling for the art of David Winter and why the collection was created.

I was born and grew up in an English village. Not a village as it would be today with telephones, television and buses, council houses with everybody having a car. A complete agricultural community. We could have almost survived with no contact with the outside world at all. We were an agricultural, almost self-supporting, unity. Each person in the village had an important part to play in making it work. No job or task was too humble for it to be denied respect. For whatever had to be done there was somebody in the community who could do it. For each played their part in making the whole work. Because of this everybody in the village had pride in being a much-needed member. If they did not do their part the complete unit would not survive. I was totally unaware of class consciousness. In the village there was no such thing. The farmer was nobody's better, nor was the squire, the thatcher, the cobbler, the weaver, or the herdsman. All took equal pride in the contribution they made. I remember on Sundays going to church. We all looked the same, for we all wore our Sunday best, the thick hand woven tweed and shiney black boots. The starched collars which were hand-me-downs, agony to wear, and all the men wore black ties. When walking to church through the village one was conscious of cottages which reflected the pride of those who lived in them. Each house was a dwelling for the life and activity that went on inside it. It reflected what went on inside by the shape and form outside. Each cottage was different because there was a different life inside it. There were strange little sheds, lean-tos, extensions, built on when the need arose. So the higgledy-piggledyness of any English village made up of these individual houses was the result of a thousand different lives, all being lived in their unique way, requiring a different accommodation to contain all that went on. Above, all, the houses exuded

a feeling of pride, because that was the strongest feeling I remember from those far off days. A sense of community, a sense of belonging — holding one's head high knowing that one had a useful craft or skill to contribute and that one could rely on everybody around the village. Sadly these days have gone for ever, but I have had a remarkable opportunity of working with David Winter on a heraldry project, and in telling David about those ancient days, he became extremely interested. He started too young to have seen for himself what I lived through but he, as an artist and sculptor, has been able to re-create a long lost feeling about how people lived, what to them and to me was the good life. His interest now covers every aspect of not only the history, of agricultural communities, but the individual crafts and skills of which they were made up. The houses he sculpts are mainly about the life that went on inside them. A craftsman with his workshop and living accommodation built around his needs. So every David Winter Cottage is about a life and a family, and an occupation, and that is why it has a feeling to it, very much the same as my feelings, as I walked down the village street to church what seems like a hundred years ago.

The cottages cover a time span from medieval England to the late nineteenth century, and consequently cover a period none of us could have experienced personally.

In my childhood I just caught the end of this period. In earlier times the social atmosphere was different than the 1930s, but the feeling of self reliance, community and village pride has always been there and in a unique way has been captured by David's work.

Brookside Hamlet
a fable

In the country was a valley, and through the valley ran a stream, with water as pure and clear as light itself. It had sparkled undisturbed over its pebbles for untold ages before a certain spring day in the year 1649. On that morning a young man named Thomas Underwood threw himself wearily on the grass beside the stream and drank deeply of the refreshing water. Despite his exhaustion, a smile spread across his face and wrinkled the corners of his eyes. He had come to the end of his search.

Thomas had just completed his apprenticeship as a miller and, being ambitious and enterprising, had left his master amid farewells and much wishing of good luck to set up his own business. In the days following his discovery of the stream, he quickly built a small shack in which to live while labouring on his main endeavour, the mill itself. He

constructed a weir to regulate the flow of the stream, directing the water against the paddles of the mill wheel. The mill building housed the grinding stones, and in time, pulleys and hoists, also powered by the water wheel, to aid him in handling the heavy bags of newly-ground flour.

When the mill was finished, Thomas began building himself a more comfortable home, a proper house with glazed windows and a fireplace. Besides providing greater comfort and security, this home would be an asset in attracting a wife and a more suitable place to raise a family.

By now Thomas was sufficiently busy to require additional help in running the mill, and this appeared in the form of Richard, the son of the shepherd in the next valley. This young man had found sheep entirely too stupid and dull, but machinery extremely interesting. And so he came to live in Thomas's original shack and to work in the mill.

In the years following, the two of them, with the help of a stonemason, made many improvements to the tiny community, including a new bridge to carry the heavily-loaded waggons. Eventually Richard finished his miller's apprenticeship and decided to build a house near the stream and offer his newly-discovered talent as a baker. The mason moved nearby because Squire Thomas had plans for a new grain storage barn. And besides, he liked Richard's fresh bread. With the arrival of a wheelwright, a tanner and a carpenter and their families, the village changed even more, although in a sense, it always remained the same. As Squire Thomas grew old and wise, he continued to enjoy the stream that had refreshed him in his youth, and which had taught him so many things. Outside his window, the water continually changed, but the stream remained the same, even as Brookside Hamlet continued to grow but always remained his home.

DAVID
WINTER

A countryman at home
amongst country folk.

"Living in the peace of the countryside suits
me, I am basically a quiet person."

"I attempt to create an 'Englishness' in my
cottages which is evocative of times and lives
now sadly gone forever."

"My family and home is very important to me;
my mother's studio has always been a refuge
and a source of inspiration."

*Faith Winter is an internationally renowned
sculptor. Her recent commissions include an
acclaimed bust of H.R.H. The Princess Anne and
the Falklands War Memorial.*

"My wife Cordelia and my children Camilla
and Edward, my work, my village — yes, I am
a lucky man . . ."

15

A Cottage Industry

Hand crafted from start to finish, David Winter Cottages are produced in the depth's of England's rural countryside.

From an idea by either David or John Hine or by inspiration from an existing building David gets down to create a new addition to the collection. Even with some of the most complicated moulding techniques available, he still has to sculpt with an awareness of the technical limitations yet without constraints on his artistic vision. The finished 'master' is then passed to mould making, and our mould making is still painstakingly all done by hand. The finished casts are then prepared for colouring and are then coloured by hand using a pigmentation formula developed by ourselves and designed to enhance the intricate detail and earthly textures of all the David Winter cottages.

The
Collection

The Village™

This is the opportunity for the collector to ramble around David Winter's incredible reconstruction of the complete community in a single piece.

Here is a flavour of every period from the 8th or 9th century to the 18th century embellishments of decorative brickwork. Take a leisurely amble up each of the little

pathways. Every step shows a
new view of continually
building interest. Those who
have owned The Village for
three years have said how
they are still discovering new
and unexpected facets of this
unique piece of art. One can
begin imagining the families
that lived in each of the
houses, from the poorest of
dwellings to the stately
prominent manor house
commanding the high ground.

Cotswold™ Village

The Cotswolds is the name given to an exquisitely beautiful area in the heart land of Britain, comprising parts of the counties of Worcestershire, Gloucestershire and Oxfordshire.

The Cotswolds are made up of dozens of little villages nestling in the folds of the Cotswold hills. The most famous feature being the stone of the area which is extremely easy to quarry. For it is so soft it lies on the surface. In order to plough a field for arable crops, the farmer first had to remove the surface stones, and the easiest place to put them was on the side of the field. But being neat-minded people they made walls out of the stone which to this day can be seen the length and breadth of the Cotswolds. These are known as dry-stone walls, for there is no bonding material used. They are supported entirely by the skill of placing one stone, so that it locks together with another. The stone is of a golden colour, and the villages on a sunny day, have a glorious aura of colour, that makes them cheerful, bright and happy. The roofs of all the houses are tiled in stone which has been split into thin slices, the largest pieces are used at the bottom of the roof nearest the gutter, the slices getting progressively smaller until the very smallest pieces lay at the ridge of the roof. This means that the greatest weight of the roof is held nearest to the outside walls, and that every piece of stone can be used, but these Cotswold stone roofs add to the overall colour of the villages. At the centre of the village stands the church, seemingly protecting the terraces of little houses around

Cotswold Village $3\frac{1}{2}" \times 6\frac{1}{2}"$ 25oz

© 1982 DAVID WINTER

it. In old England the church afforded not only the spiritual leadership of the community, but every aspect of education, and what we today call community care.

Should you visit the Cotswolds, you would be surprised at how large and elaborate many of the churches seem to be. Indeed, there must have been great wealth to have built on so great a scale. All this is because of those walls which lend the area so well to sheep farmland. During the Industrial Revolution there was an enormous demand for wool, the great majority of which came from the Cotswolds, which gave rise to great wealth — much of it spent on building beautiful churches.

23

The Village Shop™

The shop had the responsibility to stock everything that was needed, not merely for its own profit, but because villagers relied solely upon the shopkeeper to always have their needs. An enormous variety of implements and tools, and everything required for spinning, weaving and sewing. The medicines and cure-alls needed by the farmer and villagers for their animals would have been stocked, as well as the miracle remedies for ailments within the family. So much merchandise would there be that it would have been impossible to have it all inside the shop, and so in the day, on special brackets, much of the stock would be on the front, and the shop would resemble a market stall. The elaborate ridge work on the thatch roof shows that this is an important building in the community, and would very much be at the heart of the village.

The Village Shop 2¾" × 3"   6½oz

© 1982 DAVID WINTER

Little Market^{TM}

To appreciate the detail of the fine points of this piece you will need a magnifying glass to pick out the baskets of produce, game and fish. At the back you will notice the small staircase which led up to the parish chamber, where the elders of the community would meet once a month to discuss community matters. Here the squire would hold court when wrong had been done, punishment often being putting a man in the stocks — a seat with a leg trap in front of it. The poor felon had the indignity of having rotten fruit thrown at him. If pilloried, he was stood with arms and neck in a wooden trap, to disgrace and humiliate him rather than causing pain.

Little Market 3½˝×4˝ 13oz

The Parsonage™.

The Parsonage is one of the oldest of village buildings, set in lovely gardens close to the church in the centre of the community. One writer described it as "a part, not only of the village story, but of the history of England itself." One of the original roles of the parsonage was to accommodate travellers, often roving monks, or to hold a "frolic" to collect the tythe — a tax of a tenth part of annual produce of land or labour taken to support the clergy and church. Many persons were more than a little eccentric, like 18th Century gourmet/diarist John Woodforde, who after dinner once wrote: "What with laughing and eating hot gooseberry pie brought on me hiccups with a violent pain in my stomach which lasted till I went to bed." Beer formed part of the staple diet of the farmworkers and

Parson Woodforde was renowned for brewing his own, sometimes with calamitous results. One extract from his diaries reads: "Brewed a vessel of strong beer today. My two large pigs, by drinking some beer taken out of one of my barrels today, got so amazingly drunk by it, that they were not able to stand and appeared like dead things almost and so remained all night from dinner time today. I never saw pigs so drunk in my life." In the Jacobean period during the reign of James I in the 17th Century, the parsonage reflected the desire for large, spacious and well-designed buildings. They could consist of a hall, parlour, kitchen, brewhouse, milk house, and a buttery, with lodging rooms for visitors upstairs. More rooms were used for storing corn, cheese and wine, and for servants' quarters.

28

The Parsonage 9" × 9¼"   106oz

© 1984 DAVID WINTER

Stratford House™

This is an excellent example of how a building started out as one thing and, as time went by and circumstances changed, it became something completely different. Originally it would have been a very small and unimportant cottage, which would have been the home of a merchant. As prosperity increased with business success, so the building grew. As the family grew, additional parts were added on as the need dictated, and so at the end of a century or so the building is completely transformed. Stratford House, as seen here, stands as the culmination of a rich man's endeavours. It is a house of quality and would be on a par with the squire's manor house. The arrangement inside would be a central hall, wood panelled with a brick fireplace on which small trees could be burnt. This would be a room in which other local dignitaries would be entertained by the merchant habouring ambitions to be an alderman or even mayor of his community. The servants would live in the small building to the left, other than the steward, who would occupy the room close to his master's. You will see on the back a small piece of the upstairs is jutting out and this is an early example of the first indoor lavatory. It is the sort of house in which Shakespeare could well have dined when he was himself prosperous. A fine tudor building that says so much about the family who live within it.

Stratford House 4½" × 6" 32oz

The Green Dragon Pub™

Imagine going for a long walk deep in the English countryside. You leave the road and follow a little lane which peters out to no more than a footpath. You continue down this for some miles, crossing streams and stiles, through pastures and woods. Round a bend you see a ramshackle near-ruin of a house. You have arrived at the pub called The Green Dragon. The door is opened by a wizened, toothless old ancient, who beckons you in and offers you a seat on a dusty old bench in the corner. He offers you a jug of beer with china mugs to drink from. The beer is strong and warm. You offer payment and are amazed to be asked for barely a tenth of the usual price of ale. You leave and follow the path back to civilisation. This really happened to David Winter on a walk in the Yorkshire Dales with his father many years ago. Intrigued by the memory, David tried recently to find The Green Dragon pub. He walked for miles in the district where he had been on holiday with his parents, but never found The Green Dragon. Was it there? Did he dream it? David has recreated the pub from the vague memories he has of it, from that mystic day of his youth.

The Green Dragon 3½" × 4½" 15oz

Cornish Cottage^{TM}

The fierceness of the gales blowing in from the Atlantic decided the construction of Cornish houses. They had to be small, stout and firmly built. If the tiles were not thick and heavy, the wind would blow them away. The vertical slates on top of the chimneypots are there to prevent the wind blowing the smoke down the chimney and filling the whole cottage with smoke. The door would need a porch, again to protect it from the vile weather, or an outhouse for the same purpose. The Cornish love to paint their doors in bright colours. Only the hardiest of plant would grow up the walls of such a cottage, which explains why they were painted in bright and cheerful colours.

Ivy Cottage™

A little house of style with a "Grannie-, annexe" on the side, Ivy Cottage was the home of a tradesman and his family, a touch more sophisticated than an ordinary farmworker's home. The piece shows a little building to the side where the tradesman's elderly relative would live, typical of the English village where people live close enough for mutual protection, but sufficiently apart to enjoy a personal privacy. Here, the windows are more fashionable than most village homes, boasting the slightly higher status of those who live there. The village community got the spacing of the homes just right, incorporating the security of closeness lost in the uniformity of houses built in rows.

35

Alms Houses™

T he word alms means a gift to the poor and so an Alms House was a refuge for those unable to fend for themselves because of age, infirmity or sickness. The idea was that the community would build a series of small houses, so that they were able to tend for their own. Sadly, this idea deteriorated into what was in Victorian times to become the Poor House, a grim place for those who lived there in the urban sprawls that sprang up after the Industrial Revolution, a system which remained until the introduction of Social Security measures. The stylised, middle dwellings surround a large building which would have been more like an old people's home inside, and David has considered a primitive form of central heating, which accounts for the absence of chimneys.

The Alms Houses 4½" × 7"   34½ oz

Brookside Hamlet^{TM}

Brookside Hamlet demonstrates a beginning, tracing how from unoccupied open countryside, a community was born. David Winter imagined a young man trained as a miller deciding to open his own mill with money saved for years. He diverted a stream and rigged a mill wheel to harness enough power from the fast running water to drive a stone wheel to crush grain. Around this, he built a crude home in which he would store the grain, above his living area, and adapted the mill gearing to raise and lower sacks. Gradually, he would gain sufficient success to build a proper house and take a wife. As his prosperity grew, he built a better home for his family, and moved an employee into the original building. As the business progressed, he took on more employees needing little homes. Now the small community, the hamlet, was born, and in turn attracted other rural business concerns and became a village and, perhaps, grew into a town.

Brookside Hamlet 5" x 7"   41 oz
© 1982 DAVID WINTER

Sussex Cottage™

The County of Sussex lies on the south coast of England and its stone and tile cottages are typical of many parts of this rural county. The beams above the window are of stout English oak and the way in which the roof dips indicates one of the ancient beams distorting with age. The leaded light windows are made of diagonal metal containing small pieces of thick glass to shield against the relentless wind which bellows up the English Channel. Inside the cottage one can imagine the substantial fireplace in the living area with one small bedroom upstairs with perhaps a cubical for the children. These cottages delight the eye of the visitors to Sussex and are full of charm and tranquility.

40

Spinner's Cottage™

Spinning is converting brushed wool from a shorn sheep into thread using a spinning wheel, a very simple wooden foot-operated device, commonly found in the parlours of the village house. In Spinner's Cottage a group of spinster ladies or widow women would congregate each day and spin furiously. The thread would then be sold to a merchant and eventually land up in another cottage industry, which would weave the thread into tweed on a loom, again a simple but extremely effective, albeit primitive tool.

41

Fairy Tale Castle™

A place we can always imagine from Sleeping Beauty's rest to the home of Prince Charming. David's sculptural form has caught the picture we all imagine when we think of a fairy tale castle. With its friendly mystique, the place draws you in and surrounds you with warmth. The key behind the series is everyman's home is his castle, a place where you eat, sleep and raise a family, and build upon happy memories.

Fairytale Castle 10" x 6"   54oz
© 1982 DAVID WINTER

The House on Top™

This is another treat for the collector to go exploring with a magnifying glass and discovering delightful pieces of detail. The suggestion for this sculpture is that a house has been built on a sheer piece of rock jutting out from the edge of a lake. Because it is impossible to add on to the ground, the house has developed over the centuries, clinging to the rock face, supported by great beams of oak. With the passing of time the buildings have taken on a distorted shape as the wooden beams settle, giving graceful curves in the roofs and interesting bows and shapes to the walls. Notice the hefty wooden doors on the top house and feel the insecurity of people living in remote places, vulnerable to attack by travelling thugs. This house is far from the comfort and security of the village, remote and very much out on its own.

The House on Top 6" × 5" 37oz
© 1982 DAVID WINTER

Woodcutter's Cottage^{TM}

Pure fantasy seen through the eyes of David Winter, a delightful concept where a family man lives in a house which takes its shape from materials, in their natural form.

Normally a tree is felled, shaped into planks, and put up again as a house. David considers this illogical and has shown the main structure being the tree trunks. The house held up with no help from Man at all.

He has used the branches as a framework, and instead of being governed by the ground on which the house is built, he has been guided by the shape of the trees surrounding it.

Woodcutter's Cottage 6" x 4¾"   25½ oz

House of the™ Master Mason

The master mason's craft was very much a localised one, the materials he worked with to provide the building bricks and stone for village homes governed by the type he could quarry in and around his own community. Some areas of England are based on granite, some on limestone, others on sandstone — all requiring the same skills but different techniques in fashioning anything from building blocks to tombstones. And so a village in one county looked wholly different to that in the next, purely because of the type of stone it sat upon. Primarily a hand craft, the master mason's home would be lined with tools with a stockpile of stone hauled from the nearby quarry ready to be worked. Traditionally, he was equipped with many hammers and a variety of chisels, each one handed down through the generations and each designed to render a different finish to the basic stone. He could split stone at one end of the scale and chip delicately the name of a late-lamented villager on a slab to mark his grave at the other. The elaborate style of brickwork in the chimneys is the master mason demonstrating his skill and this practice is an early example of advertising. The more ornate and clever the construction indicated the mason's degree of skill.

House of the Master Mason 6½" x 5"   27½ oz

The Old Distillery™

This truly remarkable collection of buildings is where whisky is made. Whisky is made from grain and is a complicated distillation process that relies on the presence of both peat and water of a particular type. A modern distillery would be completely contained within one purpose-built factory, but David Winter's one shows how a business grew from small beginnings with bits added on as demand increased. Each building represents either part of the complicated process or accommodation for the people who worked there. The somewhat inhospitable ground on which the buildings had been built is as a result of having to put a distillery where the water is perfect for the process and before it was possible to pipe water to a factory. Peat was used in the heating process because it is so much more controllable than coal or wood and exact temperatures are critical. Of all the pieces that David Winter has created this was by far the most difficult and is as a result something of a rarity, much sort after by collectors.

The Old Distillery 9" × 10½" 140 oz

Rose Cottage™

The English countryside would not be as glorious as it is were it not for little cottages like this one, so called because of the roses cascading around the front porch and creeping across the windows. Imagine the fragrance as one approached the heavy oak front door, and the cosiness inside. The walls are made of stone, thick at the base and tapering towards the roof, which would then have been rendered with plaster and colour-washed. The chimney is the main support and one can imagine the great fireplace at its base. The thatch is like a warm blanket, keeping the family snug. Rose Cottage is, traditionally, the dream home of all newly-weds.

Cotswold Cottage™

This house so well typifies all the features of Cotswold architecture, including the over-sized corner stones running from ground to roof, and the heavy stone work, running along the edge of the roof. The window frames or mullins are all made from carved stone, with quite a lot of detail put into the over door or porch around the front door. This would be the home of a successful tradesman or merchant, standing in its own grounds, a more superior residence to the little terraced houses at the centre of the village.

Snow Cottage™

This tranquil scene of remote splendour can still be seen in England anywhere between the Pennine Mountains, which form the backbone of England, to the breathtaking beauty of the Lake District. The tiled roof could be quite easily mistaken for a thatched one as the thick virgin snow completely covers the house. At the rear, logs, neatly stacked, would be stored under cover. We can imagine the cosy nights spent here during the bleak winter months, the telling of bedtime stories as the sleepy-eyed children would look out and see the pine tree nestling against the home.

Snow Cottage 5½" × 5" 27½ oz

Market Street™

This sculpture shows three different activities. At the bottom on the left is a soup kitchen, where travellers could buy a wholesome meal of vegetable soup, strong stew laced with beer and fruit as the season's harvest offered. In the centre is the wine merchant's shop and home above and on the right the public market place where all had the right to sell their own wares. This is a typical scene of a large village or small town with shops and commercial activities centred around it. Never far from the market place would be the village scribe, always a learned man with a board across his waist held by a leather strap round his neck. It was to him people went whenever anything had to be written down, such as a bill or an agreement to a tenancy. Nearly all deals were done "on the nod" or by a shake of the hand. When written proof was advisable, the scribe did his work.

Market Street 4½" × 6¼" 27½ oz

© 1980 DAVID WINTER

The Chapel™

A Chapel is a small church or a special place set aside for worship and it was a name given by the non-conformists who broke away from both the Church of Rome and the Church of England in search of a much freer style of religion. The non-conformists built their chapels without pomp and so they are less ostentatious than the typical English countryside church. Because they were not the established religion of the country, they tended to be smaller and the atmosphere inside them more intimate.

The Chapel 6" x 4½" 22¼ oz
© 1984 DAVID WINTER

Tythe Barn™

Each year The Church would tax the village farmers ten per cent of their crops and with the money raised, give aid to the poor or any other worthy community cause.

This tax was known as 'the tythe' and the crops were stored in the Tythe Barn before being sold. It was originally a fair system, but it became so abused by unscrupulous clergymen that eventually the levy was scrapped.

Many of the barns remain across the country and are part of Britain's heritage. Most are just plain big with little or nothing lending itself to natural beauty, so David has used artistic licence and presented a farm scene, rather than just a grain warehouse. But there would be a number of farm tools around and these, along with horses in their boxes, have been remembered.

Tythe Barn 3" x 7" 25½oz

© 1981 DAVID WINTER

The Dower House™

C ustom dictated that when the village squire died, the manor house was taken over by his son and family. The squire's widow and her personal servants were required by tradition to move out to a smaller, more compact family residence, called the Dower House. From that name, the occupant took the title — still used today — of Lady Dowager. Her new home was just large enough for her to entertain friends, while at the same time being free of the problems she once had of running a large household. While still living in the manner to which she had been accustomed, the Lady Dowager could now enjoy a more tranquil life in a house built for her retirement.

Weight: 200 grams

Wine Merchant™

The Wine merchant 3½" × 4" 13oz
© 1980 DAVID WINTER

No row of shops would be complete without the Wine Merchant. Most of what he sold was produced within the community. It wasn't until comparatively recently that a licencing system came into force which prevented individuals producing their own rough beers and wines, made from every conceivable form of plant and vegetable. He would have had many sources of supply from the villagers, who would make their speciality for him to sell in the shop. One of his best lines would be a velvety black ale called Porter, so named because it had port wine added to it. Gin, commonly known as "mothers' ruin", caused a considerable amount of alcoholism, controlled finally by the imposition of savage taxation on hard liquors. Beer was not so heavily taxed and became what it is today, the favourite drink of Englishmen.

Triple Oast™

The oast exists as an essential part of the Englishmans favourite pastime of drinking beer with a bitter flavour. This special British Bitter taste comes from adding the fruit of a plant called a hop to the beer during its brewing. Hops, like grapevines, grow up special wires, to a height of 10-12ft. The fruit, unlike a grape, is feathery and made up of a large number of soft leaves. Once the hops have been harvested, they must be dried quickly in a kiln and so are taken to an oast, where they are laid out on an iron mesh floor above a great burning stove. The hot air rises up through the hops and through the cowl on the top, which revolves with the wind guided by its jutting sail, so that the air hole is always against the wind. After they have been dried, they are then pounded into sacks known as hop pockets and are then taken away by the hop merchant. He in turn sells them to the brewery. There are very few oasts in operation today as modern technology has replaced the old method, but many of the oasts have been sympathetically converted into homes and are magical places to live.

Triple Oast 5¼" × 7¼" 4½ oz

Single Oast™

This is a simplified
version of the
sculpture entitled
Triple Oast. However, in this
piece we are able to see the
open barn door and the
'pockets', or long sacks of
dried hops, waiting to be
taken away to the hop
merchant. To this day, they
are a strong, powerful feature
of the Kent countryside.
Many of these buildings have
been converted into most
beautiful homes, and one can
imagine what a pleasure it
would be to live in a converted
oast house.

Single Oast 4" x 4" 8oz
© 1981 DAVID WINTER

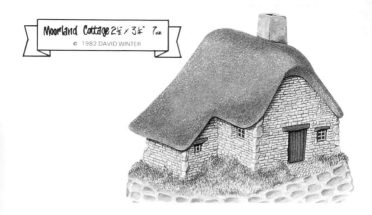

Moorland Cottage™

There are great areas of the British Isles that are called 'Moors', which means great open tracts of land, unfenced, over which herds of cattle, sheep and horses would roam, some shepherded, others virtually wild. The Moors are known as being bleak and windy, and inhospitable in the winter months. Moorland cottage is the home of a shepherd during the spring, summer and early autumn when he would have his flock roam the moors. But in the winter time the sheep would be brought down close to the village, so that they were not exposed to rigours of snow, cold and ice. The cottage is built to protect the shepherd and his family from the harsh winds, and offers very simple accommodation — one room for living and sleeping, and a small kitchen to the side.

68

Haybarn™

The hand-tied bales of hay neatly stacked in the open-fronted barn. The hay, cut during the spring and summer, will be needed in the winter to feed the cattle and horses. Beside it stands the tiny cottage, built in stone round a chimney which would house a bachelor farm worker. The inside would be furnished crudely with a table and bench, ladder-back chair and a hard wooden bed. Close to the open fire would be a dresser holding the essential eating and cooking utensils. There would be very little else inside the house apart from a cupboard in which his Sunday clothes and boots would be kept.

Tudor Manor House™

The figurehead of the community, the squire's word was the law. He gave tenant farmers the right to work his land to support their families and those of his labourers, and while the church afforded spiritual aid to the villagers, he gave them physical protection. The hereditary leader, the squire lived in the manor house and in Tudor times, marauding thieves and bandits roamed the countryside. So the manor house had to take on the role of a fortress, the main door one floor above ground and reached by a narrow staircase being easy to defend. The ground floor window in this piece would have been a later addition. Built in stone with a split stone roof, this piece has the date 1521 on the wishbone chimney which would have taken smoke from as many as eight different fireplaces.

Tudor Manor House 4" x 5½"   25oz
© 1981 DAVID WINTER

Hertford Court ™

A n imposing home for a self-made man in one of the provincial trading areas of England in the 17th Century, Hertford Court is a major town house, a symbol of the success of its owner and his influence in cities like York, Norwich and Chester. Undoubtedly a trader in a community essential to the community, he would have been elected an alderman without serious opposition, a City Father given great social standing because he provided a service for dependent townsfolk without the self-supporting attitude of rural villagers of the time. If the chimneys of this piece seem out of proportion, it is to underline an accurate observation of the period. Builders knew only how to draw the smoke from one hearth to go up one flue. Every room needed a fireplace, and all cooking was done over open fires often 10 feet wide so that sheep and sides of beef could be spit-roasted whole. The extra staircase and balcony are typical of this early urban situation, where the maximum amount of house had to be squeezed into a very limited area.

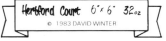

Hertford Court 6˝ x 6˝ 32oz
© 1983 DAVID WINTER

73

Tollkeeper's House™

It was customary in old
England for landowners
to charge people crossing
their territory and this fee
was called a toll. In order to
collect it barriers would be
erected along the borders of a
noble's estate and a toll
keeper employed to collect set
sums of money from all who
crossed the land. On the side
of the house the board
indicates the various amounts
that must be paid. The very
poor would make wide
diversions to avoid having to
pay anything. Much talking
would be done at the toll
gate, which formed a useful
source of information, as the
toll keeper was able to pass on
news from travellers who
passed that day in an age
before newspapers and radio.

Tollkeeper's House 6" x 6"   24oz

Cornish Tin Mine™

S cattered across the remote and often barren countryside of Cornwall, the most westerly county of Britain, can be found the ruins of the buildings that contained the beam engines which pumped the water from the mines. Tin was mined in Cornwall from the time of the Romans up until fifty years ago. At its peak employing some thirty thousand people and at the height of the industry in 1850, one in every four Cornishman was a miner. Conditions were appalling. Not only was there risks of flooding as many of the mines went far out under the sea, but the air was foul and polluted. No miner could expect to live much more than forty five years. The tragedy is that the land did not lend itself to agriculture. It was far too exposed to the Atlantic gales, men, therefore, had to take whatever employment they could get.

Cornish Tin Mine 5¼" × 3½" 11oz

The Bake House™

This is a cottage of great intrigue and one needs to explore all the nooks and crannies where David has incorporated the most amazing amount of detail. You will notice in the archway under the steps is the wood store for the bake oven and the smaller building to the right is where the flour would be kept secure from damp and rodents. The great oven lying at the base of the chimney would be a focal point of the ground floor. Here the baker kneads the dough and while waiting for it to rise, would stoke the oven until it was blazing hot. The villagers would buy their daily bread straight out of the oven. On Sundays it was customary for the baker to cook the roast in the bake oven for a bake. Instead of every fire in the village blazing away, one would use the bake house.

The Bakehouse 3¾" × 4"   10½ oz

Drover's Cottage™

The Drover was a self-employed man whose trade was to drive cattle, sheep and pigs from the farm to the market when the farmer wished to sell livestock. His helpers in this work would have been his faithful dogs, of which the most outstanding variety was the collie. The dogs would live inside the cottage, cuddled up on the hearth stone in front of the glowing embers of the fire. This cosy, comfortable little cottage would house a small family contentedly, who would have a bedroom upstairs tucked under the warming thatch of the roof. The children sleeping nearest the chimney breast. Downstairs, in the evening, the drover's wife would probably spin or weave. Not only for clothes for the family, but as something to sell in the market place, in order to bring in a little extra money. The wooden planked cottage is built firmly on to rough hewn foundations with the chimney being the main support for the floor and roof.

Drover's Cottage 2½" × 3½" 5½oz

© 1982 DAVID WINTER

Pilgrims Rest™

The religious centre of Britain is Canterbury because for more than a thousand years it has been the chosen home of the spiritual head of the church, the Archbishop of Canterbury. In the heart of the city is the Benedictine Cathedral, stupendous in architecture, glorious in its great vaulted ceiling and fine-carved stone. It was on the steps of this cathedral that the King's knights murdered Thomas Beckett, now the sacred St. Thomas. Since his death devout christians have trudged their way to Canterbury from every corner of the kingdom along paths that are to this day known as Pilgrims Ways. David Winter's cottage home is on the Pilgrims Way that lies between Winchester and Canterbury. As travellers walking across England, one would be vulnerable to attack from highwaymen, so it was therefore imprudent to carry money along the Pilgrims Way. It was the responsibility of the parishes to supply a rest home where the pilgrims could eat a frugal supper and enjoy a night's rest and this sculpture suggests such a haven. The main part of the cottage you will see is supported by a great upside down 'V' of oak beam which supports the whole building. This is known as a cruck construction, and there are several examples of this still to be found in England today.

Pilgrim's Rest 4" x 4½" 18½oz

© 1983 DAVID WINTER

The Cotton Mill™

The Industrial Revolution brought about vast changes in life style and architecture. One example of this was the Cotton Mill. It marked the change from village life and the cottage industries to a large concern with many workers. Whereas the spinner would previously make enough cotton for the village, the Cotton Mill aimed to sell its produce to the world. All food, wood, and clothes were imported from local villages, who in turn had to over produce to feed the towns. Machines were invented to help villages produce more and more and the villages in turn grew into towns.

The Cotton Mill 9"× 4½"   21 oz

The Bothy™

The iron plough was the most valued possession of the yeoman farmer, so valuable that, if he could, he would have kept it under his bed. Instead he did the next best thing and put it under the beds of the farm workers, who would only be employed so long as there was a plough to till the earth. This led to the construction of the Bothy which was on the ground floor, a shed for storing precious implements like the plough, and a kitchen. Above were small cubicle rooms in which bachelor farm workers would live. It was the custom that the wife of one of the married farmworkers would come in and prepare a hearty breakfast, and then return in the evening to prepare supper.

This tidy arrangement meant that the farm implements were totally secure, guarded by the workers, and that the men could enjoy a reasonable life with some home comforts. Marriage was not always possible for everybody as the male population always exceeded the females in Britain, except in the years immediately after 1918 and 1945. So it was a bit special to be able to attract a wife and a difficult thing to do if one didn't have a house of one's own. Collectors will enjoy looking at the archways and seeing the detail that David has shown in the oddity of places. It is also interesting to note the heavy stone support for the main beam of the cruck style of timbers used to support the roof.

The Bothy 3½" × 4" 14oz

Miner's Cottage™

This is the home of the colliery manager. He lives in grand style compared to the coal face worker who would live in a terrace of two up, two down houses. The chimneys at either end show it to be a house of sudden substance in the community affording individual bedrooms upstairs and a layout downstairs of a room for entertaining, and an eating kitchen and scullery. The colliery manager would be an important man in the community, the whole village around the mine being involved exclusively in the mining business. The owner of the mine would be a landed gentleman who would live in a country mansion, many miles from the dirt and grime of a coal mining village.

Miner's Cottage 2¾" × 3½" 5½oz

© 1982 DAVID WINTER

Fishermans Wharf™

This piece takes us back to the interesting county of Cornwall in the toe of England. The coastline is full of little coves and inlets, which made the Cornish coastline ideal for the activities of the smugglers. They could come and go almost without hindrance from the King's Customs men, who were there to see that illegal liquour, silks and spices did not get into the country without taxes being paid. Stout sailing ships would ferry the contraband from France and approach the Cornish coast, ideally on a moonless night and rowing boats would shuttle the goods to shore. Wagons under the guise of carrying legitimate crops would then be used to take them to the smugglers' secret cellars. Beneath the houses of Fishermans Wharf are caves abrim with brandy from France, silks and precious ores and metals from Germany.

Fisherman's Wharf   3¾" × 5"   15½oz

Castle Gate™

In Medieval England a community was only as secure as the stout stone wall that surrounded it. For centuries people in Britain were vulnerable to attack either by power hungry neighbours or invaders from abroad. In many parts of the country remnants of these fortifications still remain. In order to be able to get into the town, strong gates within a Gate House were built. These were the most vulnerable points of attack and were consequently most heavily defended. As time went by the necessity for such precautions became unnecessary, so the stone was taken away from the walls and used for building dwellings and so here we see an example of a medieval ruin standing proudly beside homes made from the old stone. An interesting historical collection of ideas showing again how a community has changed through its circumstances other than any design.

Castle Gate 8½" × 7¾" 51 oz

93

Squire's Hall[TM]

The squire lived in the hall, and owned the surrounding land, which gave valuable employment to many of the villagers. He was often the local member of Parliament and would with his family enjoy a high financial income, which gave them social standing in the rural community. Consequently, his home was imposing and built with the very finest oak timbers.

Squires Hall 6¾" x 5¾" 34oz
© 1985 DAVID WINTER

95

Suffolk House™

One can come across hous
with dutch end gables in mar
parts of England but they we
particularly common in th
East Anglian county
Suffolk. Influence
by that county's ag
old tradition with lo
countries and th
influx of Flemis
immigrants, th
merchant's hou
proclaimed to all th
her
indee
lived a
internation
man, a man
wealth an
tast

Suffolk House 4½" x 4"   16¾ oz
© 1985 DAVID WINTER

Hermit's Humblehome ™

Living in cluttered chaos on the edge of the village, the hermit would be the butt of ridicule and sometimes distrust by the community. Bartering with gypsies and smallholders kept him and his pony fed. To him chaos was comfortable — his fire on a winter's night, his dog at his feet, and his thoughts were enough.

Hermit's Humblehome 5¾" x 4¾" 28oz
© 1985 DAVID WINTER

DAVID WINTER™
Heart of England series
Cottages

We introduce here a new and
complete set of 10 very small
miniatures by David Winter.
The Heart of England series
sets out to capture the feeling of a
typical English Village. Not based
on any particular existing village,
these buildings or their type can
be seen all over England. In quiet
country back waters. They stand
and have done for centuries, a
serene vitality still emanating from
stone, bricks and mortar that have
seen English history and
Englishmen come and go, and the
world outside change beyond
recognition.

St. George's Church ™

To honour St. George, the patron saint of England, the solidly built stonework of the village church sprang up throughout the length and breadth of England. A place of sanctuary and peace, it is the centrepiece of English rural life both spiritually and architecturally.

St. George's Church 3" x 4½" 8 oz

© 1985 DAVID WINTER

Hogs Head Tavern ™

The village tavern was the meeting place for the men of the community. Relaxing with a jug of ale, swapping stories and gambling for small stakes, the hours of opening were at the innkeeper's discretion. There would be rooms available for overnight travellers and the Tavern would be the hub of much jollity and merry making, on special feast days and Holy days, such as May day and Harvest Festival. Many of these village inns are still in use and have kept much of their original charm.

The Hogs Head Tavern 3" x 4" 8 oz

© 1985 DAVID WINTER

Craftsmen's Cottage

In the main thoroughfare of t
village, the craftsmen's cottages
side by side closely entwined
trade as well as architecture. He
would dwell the Weaver, t
Potter, the Thatcher and Tile
Their daily toil would provide t
community with its needs. The
wares and services keeping t
village self-sufficient a
independe

Craftsmen's Cottages 2½" × 5" 8½ oz

Blackfriars Grange™

Built originally by monks of the
order of the Black Friars as part of
a larger monastery, the dissolution
of the monasteries by Henry VII
resulted in many grand
ecclesiastical buildings being given
as gifts to the nobility. Blackfriars
Grange would be the country seat
of a courtier, tended by his
steward in the absence of the lord.
It was good fortune that the
building remained intact, for
many monasteries were
demolished, their stones and
fabric being used to erect many of
the later manor houses of
England.

Blackfriars Grange 2½" × 3½" 7½ oz

The Apothecary's Shop™

The Apothecary was a chemist, physician, veterinarian and many other things beside. Inside his darkened sanctum, the villagers would be administered to with remedies based on herb lore, and ancient recipes handed down from generations past. Mysterious produce such as spices were on sale to the curious purchaser, as well as alcohol based medicines to cure their afflictions.

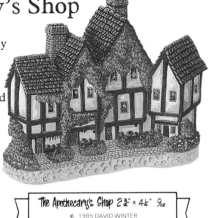

The Apothecary's Shop 2¾" × 4½" 9oz
© 1985 DAVID WINTER

Meadowbank Cottages™

On the bank of the stream, on the outskirts of the village, lie Meadowbank cottages. The home of the local landowner's gamekeeper who keeps a wary eye on his master's game (to deter the local poacher), and the gardener who tends to the landowner's grounds throughout the year.

Meadowbank Cottages 2" × 4½" 7oz
© 1985 DAVID WINTER

101

Yeoman's Farmhouse™

The Yeoman Farmer was independent. Rising before dawn and toiling until the sun went down, he would work his land with his family and provide enough produce to keep them fed with surplus to sell at market. The roof of his cottage which was low slung and thatched, dipped down to the heavy oak doors, where ivy curled and weaved its way round the windows. A small collection of livestock would provide meat, eggs and milk, and his wife would make cheeses and perhaps tend a small herb garden at the rear of the farmhouse.

Yeoman's Farmhouse 2" x 4" 7oz
© 1985 DAVID WINTER

The Schoolhouse™

The schoolhouse in the rural village was often funded by the church, and basics such as reading and arithmetic were taught. Classes were small, as only the wealthier landowners and tradesmen deemed it necessary for their children to read and write. It was not until the Civil War and the rise of Oliver Cromwell that education for the poor was acceptable.

Schoolhouse 2¾" x 4" 7oz
© 1985 DAVID WINTER

The Vicarage ™

A fine home of character for the village cleric. Besides his religious duties, he would be called upon by villagers to dispense wisdom in small disputes, to read and write letters, to give all the latest news on the King's health and foreign wars. His sons and daughters would not be taught at the village school, they would be sent away for education or he himself would provide it, or a tutor employed. Bustling with activity, a home for an intelligent man and his active family.

The Vicarage 2¾" × 4" 6¾oz
© 1985 DAVID WINTER

The Shirehall ™

The Shirehall or County hall house, the assizes and the office of the clerk of the county.
Petty misdemeanours would be dealt with by a local Justice of the Peace who would give sentences of fining or a period in the Stocks or Pillary. More serious crimes would be heard by a Circuit Judge who could wield the death penalty on more than 200 offences. Land Registration and Records office, along with County and Regional Administration were other functions practised here.

Shirehall 3" × 3½" 8oz
© 1985 DAVID WINTER

INDEX

BRITISH TRADITIONS™

A COLLECTION OF 12 PIECES BY DAVID WINTER
ONE FOR EACH MONTH OF THE YEAR

Burns' Reading Room – January

On 25th January the people of Scotland celebrate the birth in 1759 of their best-loved poet – Robert Burns. In true national style, they eat haggis, drink whisky and read aloud the words of the ploughman poet himself, to keep alive the "immortal memory". His popularity stems from the fact that he was an ordinary man who wrote poems that everyone can understand – although the Scottish dialect he uses can sometimes be a little baffling. There are many places in Scotland associated with Burns' life, but David found inspiration for his piece in an old illustration of the printing office (long gone!) in Edinburgh owned by William Smellie. Burns used to go there and sit correcting the proofs of his poems in readiness for publication. The stool he sat on was ever after known as 'Burns' stool'. The offices were actually named after their owner, but David thought 'Burns' Reading Room had a nicer ring to it!

Height: 2½"   *Length: 2¼"*   *Weight: 235g*

DAVID WINTER COTTAGES ™

The Main Collection has 36 pieces
with an additional 5 mini Collections.

The Main Collection

The Parsonage	Spinners Cottage
The Village	Kent Cottage
Little Market	The Grange
Rose Cottage	Tollkeepers Cottage
Market Street	Sussex Cottage
Triple Oast	The Green Dragon Inn
Tudor Manor House	Fisherman's Wharf
Wine Merchant	The Bothy
Single Oast	Village Shop
Squires Hall	The Dower House
Falstaff's Manor	Cotswold Village
Brookside Hamlet	Cotswold Cottage
Stratford House	Coopers Cottage
There was a	Pilgrims Rest
Crooked House	Drovers Cottage
The Bakehouse	Ivy Cottage
Castle Gate	The Chapel
Snow Cottage	John Benbow's
Hertford Court	Farm House

The Heart Of England Series

Schoolhouse	The Windmill
Hog's Head Tavern	Shirehall
Apothecary's Shop	St. George's Church
Blackfriars Grange	The Vicarage
Yeoman's	Craftsmen's Cottage
Farmhouse	Meadowbank Cottage

The West Country Collection

Cornish Harbour	Orchard Cottage
Devon Creamery	Smugglers Creek
Cornish Engine	Tamar Cottage
House	Devon Combe

The Midlands Collection

Bottle Kilns	Miner's Row
The Gunsmiths	Lacemakers Cottage
Derbyshire Cotton Mill	Lock-keepers Cottage

The Scottish Collection

The House on the Loch	Gatekeepers
Macbeth's Castle	Gillies Cottage
The Distillery	Scottish Crofters

British Traditions

Burns' Reading Room	Pudding Cottage	St. Anne's Well	Harvest Barn
Stonecutters Cottage	Blossom Cottage	Grouse Moor Lodge	Guy Fawkes
The Boat House	Knights Castle	Staffordshire Vicarage	Bull And Bush

™

John Hine Limited, 78 Woolmer Way, Bordon, Hampshire, GU35 9QE.
© COPYRIGHT JOHN HINE LIMITED 1989